MW00817887

MCKENZIE LIKES PLAYING WITH WATER

By
Deborah Naomi Eurie

Illustration: Shannika Brown

Mckenzie Likes Playing with Water

Copyright © 2021 by **Deborah Naomi**

All rights reserved. No part of this publication may be reproduced, distributed, or transmitted in any form or by any means, including photocopying, recording, or other electronic or mechanical methods, without the prior written permission of the publisher, except in the case of brief quotations embodied in reviews and certain other non-commercial uses permitted by copyright law.

ISBN 978-1-7371637-0-1

Thanks to my heavenly mother Ruth Ann Johnson for her love and strenght. She raised ten of her own children as well as the 3-20 Astoria community. Her faith made me feel like all things are possible. She is my angel and will always be with me.

Dedications:

To my father **Steven J. Romer** and my mother **Rita Romer** who pushed me to learn, create and to be the best version of myself. Thank you for your love, support and opportunities that helped me grow and be successful in life.

To my loving husband **Bernard Eurie**, whose love and encouragement has motivated me to complete this book. Bernard would tell me not to just write it but put action behind it. Thanks for always saying the right thing that encourages me to improve.

To my wonderful son's **Isaiah and Joseph Eurie**, who believed in me. They helped with the finances to publish this book and to complete my dream. I am bless to have two awesome and caring sons.

To my amazing grandkids **Brayden Murray, Malachi and Mckenzie Eurie**, whose playful actions and enthusiasm inspired me to write this book. My grandkids are a gift from God. They keep me busy and they're a lot of fun.

Acknowledgements:

To my neighbors **Mark and Jennifer Frey** and **Marie Desir**, whom I admire for their wisdom and kindness. Thanks for taking the time to edit this book.

Thanks to all my **family and friends** whose support, prayers and encouraging words has inspired me to finish this book.

Special thanks to two fabulous authors **Angela Smalls** (From The Front Pew) and **Kim Holman-Bell** (7 Prescriptions For Raising Victorious Sons), who inspired me, gave me remarkable advise and spiritual power when writing this book.

Thanks to my Lord and Savior, **Jesus Christ** for ordering my steps, giving me visions to see the impossible, the opportunity to make a difference, the courage to step out on faith and the love to care for others.

Hi my name is **Mckenzie**.
This is me when I was a baby.
I have smooth brown skin, a head full of black curly hair and
big brown eyes.

I like **playing** with **water**.
I have fun when I am **splashing** in the **puddles** of **rain**, brushing my teeth, taking a bath, helping papa wash the dishes and **swimming** in the pool.

I like **running** through the **puddles** of **water** after it **rains**.

My brother says, "Come on **Mckenzie**!" and we **run**, **jump** and splash the **water** in the air.

The **water** splashes everywhere.

My mother shouts, "No **Mckenzie**, stay out of the **water**!" She grabs my hand and pulls me away from the **puddle**. I wiggle and wiggle and pull away. **Running** back into the **puddle** of **water**, I look at her and smile. **Splash! Splash!** I would **jump** with joy

"No **Mckenzie!**" my mother shouts.
She **runs** to pick me up out of the **water**.
I laugh, "Hee, hee, hee," thinking this is a fun game for my mother and me

I like **playing** with the **water** while brushing my teeth.
My brother and I step up onto the red box to reach the **water**.

My brother puts toothpaste on my red tooth brush.

I stretch to reach my tooth brush over the **water** and swoosh it around. Then I sip the cold fresh **water**, "Sip, sip" from the tooth brush into my mouth. I keep swooshing and sipping the cool **water** over and over again.

I like **playing** with the **water** while taking a bath.
Every night before I get ready for bed, my father **runs** my
bath **water**. This is another great chance to **play** in the
water.

The clear fresh **water** was rushing down into the bathtub. He puts me into the tub. I joyfully start **playing** with the **water**, letting it **run** through my fingers. The warm **running water** feels good on my fingers.

My father puts bubble bath soap into the **water**.
"**Wow!**" More and more bubbles are floating on top of
the **water**.
I see the colors red, blue and green, like the rainbow,
floating all around me.

I put bubbles on the top of my head and blow them off my hands into the air. I **splash** the **water**, popping every bubble.

It is fun **playing** with the bubbles in the **water**.

To add to the fun, my father puts toys in the bathtub.
"Oh my!" I have baby sharks, toy animals and a yellow rubber
ducky. The baby sharks are the best toys.
I push my blue and red baby sharks down into the **water** and
watch them pop back up

I like **swimming** in the bathtub.
I lie on my stomach and move my hands and feet around.
The **water** wave moves and crashes the walls of the tub. The
water is **splashing** in and out of the tub.
This is messy and wet, but lots of fun.

I like **playing** with the **water** while washing the dishes. When my papa (grandfather) washes the dishes, I want to help.

I push the chair over to the sink. "Scrape, scrape" is the sound of the chair against the floor. Papa says, "**Mckenzie** you're so strong."
My papa looks at me with a crooked smile and helps me.

He lets me stand on the chair and I help wash the dishes. With a smile, I fill the cups up and rinse them off with the water. There is water everywhere; on the counter, floor and chair.
My clothes are wet and messy too.

My papa says, "All finished **Mckenzie**" and takes me down from the chair. I cry, wiggle and reach for the water.
"No papa, I'm not finished," so he hugs me until I stop crying.

Playing in the pool **water** is also fun.
My mother put a pretty pink bathing suit on me.

I like **swimming** in the blue pool **water** with my brothers and my cousins. I watch my brothers happily, **running** and **jumping** into the **water**.

I like the pool **water** so much; I feel free, like a fish. I like **splashing** the **water**, **running** in the **water**, **playing** with my toys in the **water** and most of all **swimming** in the **water**!

The clear blue **water** splashes everywhere, in the pool and out of the pool.

Ooh! The **water** splashes in my face and I **jump** up, squint my eyes and "Slap, slap", wiping the **water** from my eyes.

I smile and laugh, while my father and mother watches me **play**. They are delighted at how fast I am learning to **swim**.

Playing in the blue pool **water** is so much fun. **Playing** in any **water** is always a joy.

Let's do it again, tomorrow…

Title: Makenzie Likes to Play With Water

To Parents: All children learn to read at different levels. When a child continues to read, they will begin to improve their reading quaility. Word repetition and familiar words will encourage the child to like to read. This book is an educational book for children to relate too. Before the child reads this book they should review the **sight words and new words**. The sight words are basic words seen in most childrens books. The new words are words from the story and are in color. Reviewing these words should support the child to read this book more fluently.

Sight Words		New Words
a	at	Jump
he	on	Play
my	no	Puddles
me	to	Run
she	us	Splash
let	they	Swim
I	not	Water
and	now	
can	did	
with	in	
was	of	
that	go	

were	put
as	saw
look	see
are	have
up	be
it	going
is	this
the	her
him	into
an	you
get	how
like	come
would	could

The End

Made in the USA
Middletown, DE
22 November 2021

53144407R00018